THE ROYAL TYRRELL MUSEUM OF PALAEONTOLOGY

OFFICIAL GALLERY GUIDE

Canadian Cataloguing in Publication Data

Royal Tyrrell Museum of Palaeontology.
    Official Gallery Guide.

2nd ed.
ISBN 0-9697292-1-9

    1. Royal Tyrrell Museum of Palaeontology — Guidebooks.
I. Title.

QE716.C32D7 1999   560'.74'71233   C99-900752-1

Design by Blackbird Design, Calgary, Alberta
Printed in Canada by Mitchell Press Ltd, Vancouver, British Columbia

© Royal Tyrrell Museum Cooperating Society, Drumheller, Alberta. June 1999

Printed in Canada on Recycled Paper

TABLE OF CONTENTS

DIRECTOR'S MESSAGE

Palaeontology is one of the most fascinating and complex sciences. It combines geology, biology and chemistry with imagination to unravel the often tangled history of life on our planet. The discovery of a single fossil can change long-held opinions and open completely new areas for study. It can change the way we view our lives.

Ranging from prairie badlands to mountain ridges, the rocks in Alberta provide an unparalleled glimpse into the past of our province and our planet.

The Royal Tyrrell Museum is justifiably proud of its success in presenting our discoveries to so many people. This guide is an important contribution to our efforts. The product of dedicated work by many Museum staff, it provides a colourful, entertaining, review of our exhibits. We hope that this guide will enhance your experiences in the Museum and in the badlands of Alberta.

Bruce Naylor, Ph.D

Director — Royal Tyrrell Museum

ROYAL TYRRELL MUSEUM
COOPERATING SOCIETY

CHAIRMAN'S MESSAGE

Life has an incredible history. It stretches some 3.6 billion years into the past and is filled with mistakes, improbabilities, and astonishing success. The Royal Tyrrell Museum is committed to preserving and interpreting this rich history. The Museum's Cooperating Society is dedicated to facilitating these efforts. Formed in 1993 as a non-profit charity, the Society is pleased to sponsor this Gallery Guide. We hope it brings you as much pleasure as your trip to the Museum itself.

We hope that you, your family, and/or your company will consider joining with us in supporting one of the finest museums in the world. As a member of the Royal Tyrrell Museum Cooperating Society you will enjoy a variety of benefits and privileges in addition to being an active participant in the development of your Museum!

Please take a moment to review the information on the inside of the back cover and forward your membership to us. We look forward to your support. Thank you.

Ossie Sheddy

Chairman

" …To be an internationally recognized public and scientific museum dedicated to the collection, conservation, research, display and interpretation of palaeontological history with a particular emphasis on Alberta's rich fossil heritage."

**The Royal Tyrrell Museum
Cooperating Society
Drumheller, Alberta**

IN COOPERATION WITH THE
Royal Tyrrell Museum of Palaeontology
Box 7500, Drumheller, Alberta T0J 0Y0

INTRODUCTION

As far as we know, Earth is the only place in the universe where life exists.

The Royal Tyrrell Museum of Palaeontology celebrates the long history and spectacular diversity of that life. From the tiniest grains of pollen to the mightiest dinosaurs, the Museum presents an amazing diversity of ancient life.

Set in the Alberta badlands, the Museum opened in September of 1985. Four hundred thousand visitors were hoped for that first year. Nearly 600,000 came.

They came to experience the power and excitement of some of the most remarkable fossil displays anywhere, in Canada's only institution devoted entirely to palaeontology.

A LARGE AND FAIRLY PERFECT HEAD

The dusty prairie jolted the makeshift axles of
Joseph B. Tyrrell's buckboard as he
rolled towards the badlands in 1884.
A 26 year old geologist and
surveyor, Tyrrell had been sent
by the Canadian government to
map the coal and mineral
deposits of central Alberta.

In August, he and his crew
camped on the green flats
near Kneehills Creek. It
was, according to Tyrrell's
own notes, a "beautiful
green flat with wood,
water and grass in
abundance for the needs
of ourselves and our
horses". On the morning
of August 12th, Tyrrell
prospected the banks
close to his camp. There,
more than 20 meters
above the creek, he found
the remains of a dinosaur.

*A young
J.B. Tyrrell.*

It was an exciting moment, as he was to recall later. His field notes, however, maintain an objective calm: "...found a number of dinosaurian bones in an excellent state of preservation, though very brittle. Most of them were heavy and massive, but among these was a large and fairly perfect head of a gigantic carnivore."

Tyrrell's most important find, an incomplete Albertosaurus skull.

What is Palaeontology?

Palaeontology is the study of ancient life. The term comes from a combination of the old Greek words *palaios*, which means ancient, and *logos*, which means word, or reasoning.

Much of our knowledge of the ancient world comes from our study of fossils. Fossils are the remains of ancient plants and animals or the traces of their activities. Bones, shells and teeth are the best-known fossils. But many others, from footprints to fossil dung to minuscule seeds, are also on display.

Scientists do not only seek the new, the strange, the biggest. They increasingly search for clues to past environments, animal behaviour, and evolution. The smallest fossils may hold the most important clues.

[1] *Barges brought early bone hunters down the Red Deer River. Note the mosquito nets. [2] Near the current entrance to Dinosaur Provincial Park, a horse team pulls a wagonload of bones from the valley. [3] Block and tackle were used to load large blocks into wagons. [4] Modern technology has changed fossil collecting . . . a little. in 1917, the Sternbergs used tools and techniques still common today.*

Named *Albertosaurus sarcophagus*, the Alberta carcass-eater, it was the first discovery of the skull of a meat-eating dinosaur in Canada. Today, *Albertosaurus* is the symbol of the Museum that bears Tyrrell's name. The discovery site lies only a few kilometres away.

Tyrrell's find eventually sparked a rush to unearth the dinosaurs of the Red Deer River valley. It revolved around two great dinosaur hunters: Barnum Brown and Charles H. Sternberg.

People say Brown could smell a fossil before he saw it. Tipped off by an Alberta rancher, Brown visited the Red Deer River valley in 1909. He returned every summer until 1915, collecting fossils with outstanding results.

In order to prevent the loss of invaluable fossils to foreign institutions, the Canadian government equipped a collecting party in 1912. At its head was Charles Hazelius Sternberg, an independent collector who had supplied impressive American specimens to institutions around the world. He brought his three sons – Charles M., George and Levi – with him.

What the Sternbergs and Brown hauled out of the Red Deer River valley in the next three years outshone all previous collections of Cretaceous dinosaurs – fossils in superior condition still displayed in museums around the world.

Although the badlands were to feel the picks and hammers of the bone hunters after 1917, the great Canadian dinosaur rush was over.

How Fossils Are Collected

Dinosaurs don't find you, you have to find them. Sometimes you get lucky and stumble across a spectacular find when you least expect it. But usually, finding a dinosaur and digging it up is a long, hard job.

Collectors spend hours hiking the badlands along the Red Deer River, scanning the rock strata for fragments of bone.

When a specimen is found, collectors dig around it. They use jackhammers, picks and shovels to remove overlying rock. Sometimes, dynamite blasts away hard rock. Closer to the specimen, more delicate tools are used.

Stabilizers are applied to the fossil to keep it from breaking apart. A jacket made of layers of burlap and plaster of paris is wrapped around the exposed specimen. A trench is dug around the fossils, the block is flipped over, an the bottom is also jacketed.

Wrapped in their protective jackets, fossils are transported to the Museum's lab, where they will be prepared and carefully studied.

It Takes Time

The marvellous invention that is life on Earth has survived for more than 3.5 billion years. The planet itself is over a billion years older. It has taken a long time for the Earth and its life to develop into what we know today.

Just as our lives are measured in years, days and hours, geologists measure time in **eras**, **periods** and **epochs**. Significant events are often turning points in our lives, and geologists use significant events in the history of life on Earth to mark important divisions of geologic time. The geologic time scale is one of the most important tools we have in understanding the life of the past.

GEOLOGIC PERIOD

Quaternary Period
Recent
Pleistocene — 2

Tertiary Period
Pliocene
Miocene
Oligocene
Eocene
Palaeocene — 65

CENOZOIC ERA

Cretaceous Period — 135

Jurassic Period — 181

MESOZOIC ERA

Triassic Period — 230

Permian Period — 280

Carboniferous Period — 345

Devonian Period — 405

Silurian Period — 425

PALAEOZOIC ERA

Ordovician Period — 500

Cambrian Period — 600

Precambrian

M I L L I O N S O F Y E A R S A G O

PRECAMBRIAN ERA

12

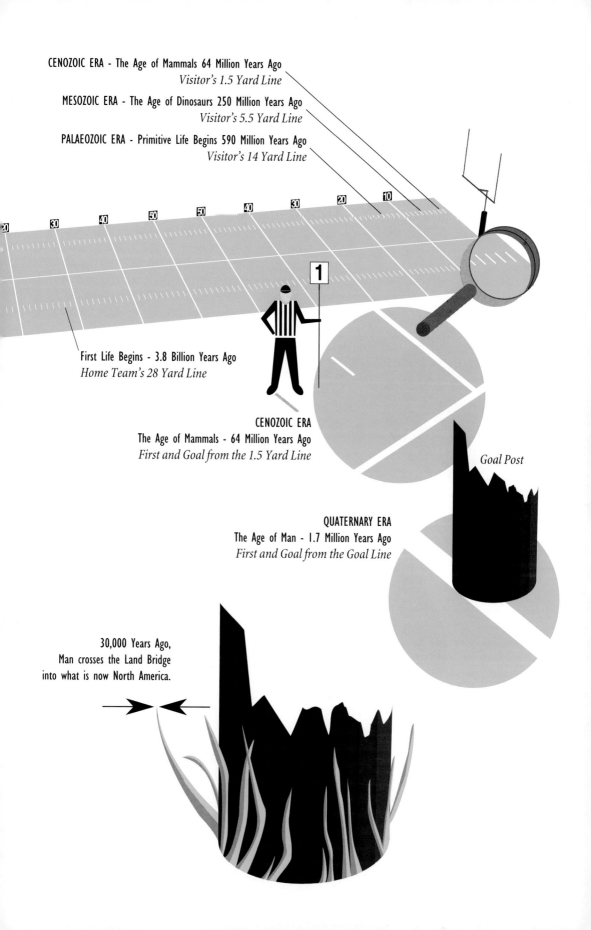

CENOZOIC ERA - The Age of Mammals 64 Million Years Ago
Visitor's 1.5 Yard Line

MESOZOIC ERA - The Age of Dinosaurs 250 Million Years Ago
Visitor's 5.5 Yard Line

PALAEOZOIC ERA - Primitive Life Begins 590 Million Years Ago
Visitor's 14 Yard Line

First Life Begins - 3.8 Billion Years Ago
Home Team's 28 Yard Line

CENOZOIC ERA
The Age of Mammals - 64 Million Years Ago
First and Goal from the 1.5 Yard Line

QUATERNARY ERA
The Age of Man - 1.7 Million Years Ago
First and Goal from the Goal Line

Goal Post

30,000 Years Ago,
Man crosses the Land Bridge
into what is now North America.

The Changing Earth

Over time, the Earth itself has changed dramatically. Its surface is constantly recycled, as exposed rock weathers, breaks down and is carried away by wind and water to be deposited as sediment. After long periods of time, the sediments are transformed into sedimentary rocks and the process begins anew.

Other processes are at work too. The Earth's crust has been in constant motion since its formation 4.6 billion years ago. Fractured into a patchwork of plates and floating on currents of molten rock beneath, the plates collide and pull apart.

This process is called **continental drift**. Its stately unfolding explains long-standing puzzles about the distribution of modern and ancient life. It also helps us to understand past environments.

The continents aren't the only things to have changed. The Earth's climate has modified dramatically over time. Chemical changes in the oceans continue to affect many living things. Even the air we breathe is radically changed from that enjoyed by earlier inhabitants of the planet.

*Early in the Earth's history, all the continental plates had joined to form a large super-continent known as **Pangaea**.*

*By the **Mesozoic Era**, Pangaea had begun to break up. The break-up led to many changes, including the isolation of dinosaur populations in many parts of the world.*

The modern world is still in motion. North America drifts closer to Asia, and the movement creates the volcanoes and earthquakes that plague the countries of the Pacific Rim.

Evolution

Evolution is the continuing change of species through time. It is a crucial concept in our understanding of how the world has come to be what it is today.

The Earth challenges the skills of living things. They must survive. If an individual varies from the norm, its differences may limit its success or may enhance its ability to make the most of its environment. In the latter case, the individual may pass beneficial new traits along to its offspring. As the differences mount up through time, new species evolve.

But even as new species evolve, others disappear. Extinction is part of the process of evolution. We often wonder what happened to the dinosaurs, but the extinction of the dinosaurs was not an unusual event. In fact, more than 90% of the species that have inhabited the Earth have long since disappeared.

Becoming An Oyster

Evolutionary change can be traced in some detail in many organisms. Dr. Paul Johnston of the Royal Tyrrell Museum has been studying the changes in oysters and their ancestors over the millennia.

1. Catamarcaia chaschuilensis

2. Umburra cinefacta

3. A new species

4. Texigryphaea sp.

Early Ordovician (475 million years old), Argentina. The two halves of shell are of equal convexity. The animal burrowed vertically into the muddy sea bottom.

Middle Silurian (415 million years old) Australia. The right half of the shell is a little less convex than the left half. The animal likely burrowed into the muddy sea bottom at an angle with the left side undermost.

Early Devonian (390 million years old) Australia. Currently under study at the Royal Tyrrell Museum, the right half of the shell is much less convex than the left half, and has widely spaced concentric frills. This animal was a shallow burrower and lay on its left side on the sea bottom.

Early Cretaceous (100 million years old), Texas. This is a gryphaeid oyster. The right half of the shell is nearly flat with closely spaced concentric frills. The left half of the shell is strongly convex. The animal lay on its left side on the sea bottom. It was immobile and the left half of the shell became very thick and heavy to keep it in place on the sea floor.

THE PRECAMBRIAN

4.6 billion to 590 million years ago

A whorl of stars against the blackness, a disc-like galaxy turns in the heavens. In each of us is the slightest trace of stardust.

The Big Bang, and After

The Earth is some 4.6 billion years old. How do we know that, and where did it come from?

Observations show that all the heavenly bodies are receding from one another at a great rate of speed. This has led astronomers to suggest that the known universe originated with an immense explosion, known as the Big Bang. Since that event some 15 billion years ago, the universe has been constantly expanding.

Clouds of interstellar dust and gas, tattered, blown and compressed by galactic explosions, occasionally coalesced into dense masses held together by gravity. These masses became stars. The same processes are at work today, forming new stars in the vast heavens.

The Earth and the other planets probably formed from small rocky bodies called **planetisimals**. Swirling in a disc-like cloud around a gassy core that would become the Sun,

16

the planetisimals eventually gathered into bigger and bigger bodies. As they grew larger they moved at higher speeds, colliding with greater impact, sometimes fragmenting, sometimes joining together in a process known as accretion.

The bodies that joined together became planets. Some of the fragments became meteorites, which even today collide with the Earth. Debris blasted away from the Earth by a major collision may have given rise to a particle cloud that eventually formed the Moon. Dating of lunar rocks shows them to be almost 4.5 billion years old. They were formed shortly after the Earth's crust began to take shape.

First Life — Precambrian Time

The Precambrian Era is the longest division of geologic time, but it is the one we know least about. It began with the formation of the Earth's crust some 4.6 billion years ago and saw many important changes to the young planet. We do know one very important additional fact. Life, however poorly preserved, began during the Precambrian.

It probably appeared in shallow, nutrient-rich waters some 3.8 billion years ago. The earliest known fossils are remains of single-celled bacteria. Living things with more than one cell appeared much later. They appear in rocks some 700 million years old, although their diversity suggests they evolved earlier.

Some Precambrian rocks are known in Alberta. They suggest that this province was at times a stark wind-swept landscape, inhospitable to any life. At other times, shallow seas covered parts of the province, bringing with them the first organisms to inhabit this part of the world.

Stromatolites are among the earliest known fossils. Their many-layered look results from alternating bands of sediment and algae.

For many years, stromatolites were known only as fossils. Recent discoveries of living stromatolites like these in Shark Bay, Australia, confirmed growth patterns and internal structure.

The blue-green planet, Earth is awash with water, atmosphere and life. Background: A reproduction of banded iron Precambrian rock shows alternating layers of oxidized and non-oxidized iron, suggesting that an oxygen-rich environment was cyclical.

A Place with Atmosphere

The Earth didn't always have an atmosphere, and it certainly didn't always have this one. Its first atmosphere was a gathering of interplanetary gases attracted by the Earth's gravity. Hydrogen and helium were prominent among them. This first atmosphere would have been lethal to most life as we know it.

The first atmosphere was washed away from the Earth by the solar wind. A second atmosphere was created by out-gassing from the planet itself. Rich in carbon dioxide, which early plants transformed into oxygen, this secondary atmosphere is the one in which contemporary life flourishes.

THE PALAEOZOIC ERA

590 – 250 million years ago

Volcanoes and other mountain-building events characterized the end of the Precambrian. But even in the more placid early Palaeozoic, land was an inhospitable place for life. The earth was rotating faster, and the tides were more powerful. There was no vegetation. Shallow seas advanced and retreated over the continents.

Ancient Life

The Palaeozoic Era began 590 million years ago with the appearance of diverse multi-celled organisms with preservable hard parts. In fact, the evolution of single-celled organisms into many-celled creatures, which had occurred in the Precambrian, was a major evolutionary step.

The Palaeozoic seas teemed with life. But typical Precambrian life forms such as worms and jellyfish were soft-bodied and rarely preserved. Hard body parts have a far greater chance of being preserved as fossils than do soft body parts.

The development of hard parts was probably made possible by changes in the chemical composition of the oceans. It was a major change. Skeletons provide a solid support for muscles and organs, allowing animals to move faster and grow larger. Shells and external skeletons protect from predators, while hard mouth parts make more efficient feeders.

Preservable hard parts account for a much-improved fossil record in the Palaeozoic. Trilobites, brachiopods and many other invertebrate animals provide much data about the changing world of the Palaeozoic.

Although the early seas were filled with life, the land was at first barren. But by the end of the Era, plants and insects flourished on land, as did amphibians and the first reptiles. This richness was devastated, however, at the end of the Palaeozoic, by the worst extinction the Earth has ever witnessed.

Paradichorinus planus, a Carboniferous crinoid found in Indiana, more commonly known as a sea lily, was related to starfish and sea urchins.

CAMBRIAN, ORDOVICIAN & SILURIAN PERIODS
590 – 410 million years ago

These three periods make up the first half of the Palaeozoic Era. They witnessed a great burst of evolutionary development, with new and unusual creatures stocking the Earth's oceans.

For much of this time, southern Alberta was covered by a shallow sea, as were many parts of present-day continents. A host of shelled invertebrates swarmed in the seas. **Echinoderms**, with skeletons of hard, connected plates, became abundant. Many animals that live in colonies, including the first true corals, appeared. **Trilobites**, relatives of the modern horseshoe crab, were diverse and abundant.

Favosites are Colonial Corals from the late Ordovician (440 million years ago) found near Cranbrook, B.C..

Fish first appeared early in the Palaeozoic. Lacking jaws, they sucked water and sediment into their mouths, straining food from the mud. In time they spread throughout the seas, evolving into many forms. Many fish became active, streamlined swimmers, adapted to life in the open ocean.

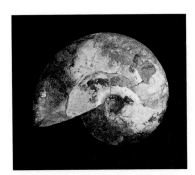

The elegantly curled shell of an ammonite carries evidence about its internal structure in its suture marks. Common for much of the Palaeozoic, ammonites disappeared at the end of the Cretaceous.

The first life on land appeared during this time as well. Land plants became common in the Silurian Period. Insects too had become widespread. Millipede burrows and scorpion remains are evidence of their presence.

The first land plants and animals faced similar problems. They had to find ways to keep from drying out, support their weight, and obtain oxygen from the air.

Plants adapted to conditions away from water, in part, by developing vascular systems to conduct water and nutrients through their roots, stems and branches.

Even as they changed to adapt to the land, they changed the land around them. Before land plants, there was no soil. Land plants broke down rock and contributed their own decaying remains to the mixture. They anchored the soil with their roots, thus making the land more hospitable for other kinds of life.

Palaeozoic Pillars

The tallest organisms ever to stand on the sea floor, sponge-like creatures known as stromatoporoids were recently collected by Museum staff from Top-of-the-World Provincial Park near Cranbrook, B.C.

Some 440 million years old, these giant pillar-like animals grew on the bottom of a deep, tropical sea. They did not have branches and were without roots. Researchers think they balanced precariously on the bottom mud and may have toppled over easily, especially when severe storms stirred the bottom.

Trilobites

Trilobites were marine invertebrates with three-lobed shells. They appeared at the beginning of the Palaeozoic.

Among the first animals to develop hard skeletons over their bodies, trilobites left large numbers of fossils around the world. Many have been found in clusters, probably the remains of shells shed prior to mating. Their tracks also survive as fossils.

They protected themselves in many different ways. Some burrowed into the mud. Others evolved spines, or the ability to roll up in a tight ball. Several species grew too large for predators to handle.

Even so, they all became extinct. Their relatives are common in our world however. Eighty per cent of all living animals share a common ancestor with trilobites.

THE BURGESS SHALE

Soft body parts rarely fossilize well, but the 530 million year old Burgess Shale, now exposed high on Mt. Field in British Columbia, preserves the remains of a multitude of soft-bodied animals.

Although it is uncertain as to the exact circumstances that led to the preservation of this marine community, it may once have lived on the mud at the edge of an undersea cliff. Animals carried over the cliff by currents or mudslides died in the deeper, colder, oxygen-poor water at the bottom. Lack of oxygen prevented the soft-bodied animals from decomposing.

The Burgess Shale fossils are rare and exquisitely preserved. Among the oddities are *Opabinia*, a segmented animal shorter than your finger with long flaps hanging from its sides, five mushroom-like eyes, and a long nose with claws on it, and *Hallucigenia*, a many-tentacled creature which continues to baffle scientists.

It's unlikely the Burgess Shale community was unique. These animals were probably common in the Palaeozoic seas but many of them have only been fossilized here, in this unusual rock.

The PanCanadian Burgess Shale Exhibition features 46 species of strange creatures represented in models before and beneath you.

No bigger than a fingernail, a streamlined Marella, one of the most common Burgess Shale creatures, glides across the sea floor.

Visitors inspect the Burgess Shale Quarry under the watchful eye of guide Rosemary Power.

THE DEVONIAN PERIOD
410 – 360 million years ago

The Museum's Devonian exhibit features corals and other reef-building animals.

The Devonian Period has been termed the Age of Fishes because of the great proliferation of fish species throughout the oceans of the world.

The first detailed record of vertebrates comes with the evidence of jawless fish. These bottom-dwellers, some of which had skeletons made of cartilage rather than bone, first appeared some 500 million years ago. Many were covered in plate-like armour.

Jawless fish declined as jawed fish appeared. The latter, efficient swimmers and toothsome feeders, came to dominate the oceans of the Devonian. They evolved into many forms, including 9 meter long Dunkleosteus, the largest predator of its time.

The Devonian also witnessed great expansion of life on land. Plants and invertebrates were already well established, but it was during the Devonian that the first vertebrates made the transition. In a kind of evolutionary halfway house, they were caught between land and water. These **amphibians** inherited lungs from an air-gulping ancestor closely related to the modern coelacanth. They managed to stump over the lowlands on their fin-like limbs.

The largest predator of the Devonian seas, Dunkleosteus is known from only scattered remains in Alberta.

Canowindra, one of 114 fish on a slab of rock from Australia, this skeleton provides clues to the transition of vertebrates to land.

Although early amphibians were able to survive on land, reproduction tied them to the water. Most amphibians, then and now, must lay their eggs in water. Many of the early amphibians continued to live largely or exclusively in water.

For Alberta the Devonian Period was a critical one. Much of the province's conventional oil and natural gas reserves are found in Devonian rocks. At the time, Alberta lay under a warm, shallow sea. Reefs developed, forming the porous reservoirs for the oil that we pump from below the surface. Elsewhere, in southern Saskatchewan, the same sea became very salty and vast deposits of potash were formed.

Vuggy Dolomite – Bulbous stromatoporoids in this reef rock have been leached at there centres leaving spaces called vugs. The vugs were later filled with coarse, white, dolomite crystals that usually fall out when exposed to erosion. In the subsurface, vuggy dolomite may be saturated with petroleum.

THE CARBONIFEROUS AND PERMIAN PERIODS
360 – 250 million years ago

The Carboniferous Period gets its name from the Latin words for "carbon-bearing", a name first applied to coal-rich rocks in England. The coal is a product of vast swamps that covered many parts of the world, particularly in Europe and eastern North America, at this time.

Winging through the swamps were incredible insects. Extraordinarily large dragonflies flew through the humid air. On the damp ground crawled worms, slugs, millipedes, and their rapidly-spreading slimy colleagues. Today, there are more insect species that all other animal species put together.

The earliest reptiles appeared in the Carboniferous. They broke the direct tie all vertebrates had up to that time with water. They lived and reproduced entirely on land. The earliest reptiles were small enough to nest in your hand, but gave rise to diverse lines, one of which would produce birds and dinosaurs.

A great variety of crinoids have arisen through geologic time. Although animals, they had a flower-like appearance. Most clung to the sea floor by means of a stem, although a few were free-swimming.

29

Another line of early reptiles ultimately gave rise to mammals. These mammal-like reptiles achieved early success, dominating the world for millions of years before dinosaurs arrived on the scene.

Near the end of the Palaeozoic, global changes brought hardship and an astonishingly widespread extinction. The slow drifting of the continents united all the land masses of the Earth together in one huge super continent – Pangaea. Its interior grew drier, experiencing cooler winters and hotter summers.

Glaciers advanced and sea level slowly fell. Alberta, which had been underwater for much of the Palaeozoic, gradually was lifting above sea level. Shallow marine environments surrounding the continents came under enormous stress and some disappeared entirely. Nine out of every ten species of invertebrates died. Their passing marks the end of an era of Earth history.

Insect Explosion

Today, some 900,000 insect species inhabit this planet, more than the total of all other animals species combined.

Insects first appeared about halfway through the Palaeozoic Era. Extremely large forms, some bigger than hawks, quickly evolved. Many eventually developed a life cycle in which individuals went through remarkable changes as they grew. Dragonflies, which grow from egg to larva to nymph to adult, are a modern example of this process.

The fossil record of insects is not good. Their thin, brittle external skeleton breaks down quickly after death. The best insect fossils have been found smothered in layers of volcanic ash or beautifully embedded in amber, the hardened resin of coniferous trees.

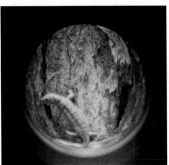

A peephole in time discloses one of the earliest-known reptiles hiding in a tree stump from Nova Scotia.

30

Dimetrodon

Dimetrodon was an early mammal-like reptile, the top predator of its time. Its sail was probably an early experiment in thermo-regulation. In the morning, turned sideways to the sun, the blood vessel-rich sail would rapidly heat the body, allowing *Dimetrodon* to become active before other animals. If too hot, the animal could face into the sun, radiating excess heat from the sail.

Eryops was a large carnivorous amphibian

THE MESOZOIC ERA

250 – 64 million years ago

One of the most dramatic views of dinosaurs anywhere, the mezzanine viewpoint at the Royal Tyrrell Museum reveals some 35 dinosaurs from around the world.

THE AGE OF DINOSAURS

The Mesozoic is made up of three periods – Triassic, Jurassic and Cretaceous. Together, they make up the Age of Dinosaurs.

In many ways, the Mesozoic Era parallels the Palaeozoic, beginning with an expansion of new life forms. It opened with the continents united as a single land mass. As smaller continents broke free, sea levels rose and the climate moderated. Its end, however, was marked once again by a massive extinction.

Few rocks from the Triassic and Jurassic periods are exposed in Alberta. However, this province's Cretaceous rocks are among the world's richest fossil resources.

The Mesozoic Era is introduced by the **Palaeoconservatory**. To enter, look carefully for the plate glass doors at the end of the Permian exhibit. The Palaeoconservatory is a collection of plants found in southern Alberta during the last phase of the Age of Dinosaurs. Little-changed descendants of primitive plants have been brought together from the southeastern United States, South East Asia and elsewhere. They provide a striking contrast to the dry, barren badlands of modern Alberta.

A Camarasaurus mugshot shows off the chisel-like teeth of this relatively small sauropod from Utah.

THE TRIASSIC PERIOD
250 – 210 million years ago

Two great Dinosaur orders evolved during the early Mesozoic: Saurischian (lizard-hipped) and Ornithischian (bird-hipped).

Plants and animals that inhabited the Triassic world were survivors. They had pulled through the great extinction that marked the end of the Permian and carried on to re-populate the world.

As the Mesozoic began, large crocodile-like amphibians still prowled the margins of lakes and swamps. Mammal-like reptiles were well established. They would give rise to mammals just before the Period ended. Although successful, mammals would be dominated by the dinosaurs for 150 million years. They remained tiny, many living a precarious nocturnal existence, hiding from the flesh-eating dinosaurs.

From primitive reptiles called thecodonts arose three distinct reptilian lines: crocodilians, flying reptiles, and dinosaurs. The flying pterosaurs are extinct, but both crocodiles and dinosaurs remain with us. Crocodiles have changed little in their long history, while dinosaurs were transformed into birds.

Albertosaurus, a Cretaceous carnivore, represents dinosaurs with a lizard-like pelvis that developed early in the Mesozoic Era, along with those having the characteristic bird-like pelvic structure of most plant-eaters.

Plants with a Past

During the time of dinosaurs in Alberta, lush plant growth supported some giant appetites. The Museum's 345 meter-square Palaeoconservatory gives an idea of what some of that vegetation was like.

Some of the 118 species here have changed little in 180 million years or longer. Many grew in Alberta 70 million years ago when the climate was much like Florida's today. In fact, several species planted here come from Florida, as well as California, Malaysia, Singapore, Australia and New Zealand.

Dinosaurs walked tall. The legs of more primitive reptiles splay out to the sides like those of a lizard. Dinosaurs stood and moved with their legs directly under the body, as birds and large mammals do today. With this support system, dinosaurs could grow tall and heavy and retain their mobility, on four legs or two. Some dinosaurs that walked on all fours grew to enormous size, the largest animals ever to live on land. Of the two-legged dinosaurs, carnivorous giants like *Albertosaurus* and *Tyrannosaurus rex* still have power to frighten us today.

While dinosaurs were developing, Alberta was under water. Just over the border in British Columbia, the mountain slopes around Wapiti Lake yield examples of the kinds of creatures that would have swam where Drumheller now stands.

Primitive **ichthyosaurs** and other marine reptiles returned to the aquatic existence abandoned by their ancestors millions of years before. They shared the seas with abundant fish. Their remains have been found in several parts of western Canada, including Wapiti Lake and the oil sands at Fort McMurray.

Ichthyosaurs evolved into large, fast-swimming creatures like this Cymbospondylus from Nevada. Few other reptiles have adapted so well to life in the water. Built like dolphins, ichthyosaurs could dive deeply to pursue fish.

Dilophosaurus was a typical early carnivorous dinosaur.

Heterodontosaurus, an early herbivorous dinosaur was about the size of a modern-day turkey.

The Wapiti Lake Window

Fossils from the remote Wapiti Lake region of northern British Columbia provide a window to the marine environment of the Triassic Period.

First discovered in 1947, collected in 1961 – 62 and again in the 1990s, the fossils include many fish species and several kinds of marine reptiles. Related fossils have been found in widely scattered localities.

During the Triassic, most of the Continental plates, including western Canada, Madagascar and Greenland were part of one large land mass. But the land mass broke up and drifted apart, separating its marine communities. Today, we find similar Triassic fossils in widely separated locations.

The Jurassic Period
210 – 140 million years ago

Camarasaurus stretches upward to reach high-growing vegetation. Like all other sauropods, Camarasaurus was a herbivore, and it probably had to browse constantly to maintain its optimum body weight..

The Jurassic was a time of dramatic change on the North American continent. The land was gradually being pushed up out of the sea and dinosaurs flourished everywhere. Winding rivers drained the highlands, carrying sediment to the shallow, muddy sea that still covered the continental interior. It too teemed with life.

Jurassic dinosaurs ranged from the size of a chicken up to nearly the size of a blue whale, the largest living thing alive today. Although Alberta only has marine rocks of Jurassic age, fossils from the United States show the great diversity of dinosaurs that lived in North America during this period.

The skull of the Jurassic killer Allosaurus bites down on the skeleton of a hapless Camptosaurus.

Sauropods were common Jurassic dinosaurs. All walked on four legs, supporting immensely long necks and tails.

At only 18 metres in length, *Camarasaurus* was shorter than many sauropods. It was one of the more common Jurassic dinosaurs in western North America.

The 27 metre length of *Diplodocus* was mostly neck and tail. Peg-like teeth at the front of its mouth interlocked so it could rake leaves and twigs from branches.

Supersaurus, known only from isolated finds such as the shoulder blade on display at the Museum, may have been up to 30 meters long.

Large flesh-eating dinosaurs also inhabited the world of the Jurassic.

Growing up to 12 metres in length, *Allosaurus* was the most common carnivorous dinosaur in Jurassic North America. Smaller meat-eating dinosaurs may have hunted in packs or scavenged the kills of the larger predators.

Less than eight metres long, *Stegosaurus* may have cooled its blood with its tall bony back plates, while using its spiked tail for defense.

Related to the duck-billed dinosaurs of Alberta's Cretaceous, *Camptosaurus* grew to seven meters long and walked on all fours.

Easily recognized with their plate-lined backs, stegosaurs are among the best-known Jurassic dinosaurs. The plates may have helped to regulate the animal's body temperature. A notoriously small head and spikes on the tail are other typical features.

The Mesozoic Era saw many creatures take to the air. The insects had been there for millions of years. By the end of the Triassic Period reptiles were taking to the air as well. And not long behind them were the first birds.

The *pterosaurs*, or "wing lizards", appeared in the Triassic and survived until the extinctions at the end of the Cretaceous Period. Perhaps their flight evolved as they glided from trees, or perhaps they took to the air by leaping after insects.

A reconstructed Quetzalcoatlus swoops over the Museum's dinosaur hall.

Some, like *Quetzalcoatlus*, known from Alberta and other parts of the world, had wingspans as big as a small plane. They were the largest self-powered fliers ever.

Some 150 million years old, *Archaeopteryx* is the first known bird. In many ways it resembles a dinosaur. Its skeleton is like the skeletons of many small dinosaurs, and it has sharp teeth. But it has a wishbone and, most importantly, feathers.

THE CRETACEOUS PERIOD

140 – 64 million years ago

Cretaceous North America was a very different place. Viewed from space, it would appear as two continents separated by a narrow sea stretching from the Gulf of Mexico to the Arctic Ocean. Alberta was situated on the western shores of this shallow inland sea, sometimes a broad lowland area, sometimes under water.

Rivers flowed eastward from the western highlands to the sea, depositing sediments along the way. They meandered across a coastal plain, where the climate was warm and swamps and forests prevalent.

This low, river-laced environment had its hazards. Large predatory dinosaurs were fast and agile, armed with sharp teeth and claws. Disease and injury took their natural toll. Some fossils indicate that large groups of animals died at the same time, probably from some natural calamity such as a flood.

One bonebed in Dinosaur Provincial Park contains the remains of at least 50 horned dinosaurs. Some scientists think that these animals may have died trying to ford a flood-swollen river.

Although the Cretaceous Period always brings to mind the large dinosaurs, that ancient world contained much more. Just as today the small creatures – mice, frogs and rabbits – outnumber the large, the same was true in the world of the dinosaurs.

The lowlands of Alberta were inhabited by many species of mammals, frogs, salamanders, lizards, turtles, crocodiles and fish. Although some of these, most notably the mammals, have changed radically, others have changed little or not at all.

Full Flower

The Cretaceous Period saw rapid development and spread of **angiosperms**, or flowering plants. Able to mature and reproduce more quickly than other plants, the angiosperms spread to every continent and made inroads into every type of environment.

Angiosperm means "enclosed seed" and angiosperms enclose their unfertilized seeds in a protective envelope called an ovary. When the egg is fertilized, it has a safe, nurturing environment in which to grow. Sound familiar? Humans do it the same way.

Complex leaves and, of course, flowers are additional features of the angiosperms. Not all flowers are immediately apparent. Grasses, perhaps the most important food plants in the world today, are angiosperms.

Most dinosaurs laid eggs, and the nests drew predatory dinosaurs like Dromiceiomimus. Like most ornithimimid dinosaurs, this predator was long-limbed and agile.

Left to Right: Centrosaurus apertus,
Arrhinoceratops brachyops, Chasmosaurus belli,
Triceratops sp.

Horns and Frills

Ceratopsians, or horned dinosaurs, were among the last dinosaur groups to evolve. Large and powerful, they may have ranged in herds across the North American interior. Their great variety of horns and neck frills may have protected them from predators but may also have been used to threaten rivals of their own species.

44

One of the last and yet one of the most primitive dinosaurs to have lived in Alberta, *Leptoceratops*, was a horned dinosaur without a horn.

Triceratops was the last and largest of the horned dinosaurs.

Chasmosaurus was a common Alberta ceratopsian with a long frill and short horns.

The remains of more than 50 *Centrosaurus* individuals have been found in a single site in Dinosaur Provincial Park.

A Chasmosaurus skeleton is displayed in the foreground while the painted mural backdrop shows a group of these Ceratopsians grazing in their habitat

Prosaurolophus one of Alberta's largest hadrosaurs.

Hadrosaurs

Based on the numbers of their remains, duckbilled dinosaurs must have been very common in Late Cretaceous Alberta. Named for their flattened toothless beaks, duckbills were plentiful and diverse, perhaps moving in large herds across the landscape.

Behind the beak were batteries of hundreds of cheek teeth adapted to chewing tough plant material. The teeth were replaced throughout life. Most hadrosaurs weighed about as much as an elephant, although a few were larger.

Edmontosaurus was one of the latest and largest duckbills in Alberta. It is a flat-headed duckbill with no crest on the skull.

Prosaurolophus is known from southern Alberta 75 million years ago. The small knob on top of its skull, just in front of its eyes, developed into a solid spike in its descendants.

Named for Lawrence Lambe, one of the early fossil hunters in the Red Deer River Valley, *Lambeosaurus* had a large, hollow, hatchet-shaped crest.

The distinctive hump on the broad bill of *Kritosaurus* reminded early scientists of a Roman nobleman's nose. Its name means noble lizard.

Devil's Coulee

The first nests of dinosaur eggs in the province were uncovered by the Royal Tyrrell Museum in southern Alberta in 1987. In an attractive three-pronged cut on the Milk River Ridge known as Devil's Coulee, the remains of a duckbill nesting site created an international sensation.

Most of the eggs found probably belonged to *Hypacrosaurus*, a common Alberta duckbill. The eggs are about the size of a modern emu's and were laid in circular nests. Anywhere from 12–24 eggs were in each clutch, which the adult dinosaurs covered with rotting vegetation in order to aid hatching.

The nesting site provided additional evidence to the suggestion that many dinosaurs were social animals, moving in large herds and gathering in particular locations to hatch and raise their young.

Male *Parasaurolophus* had a long crest extending 2 meters behind the skull. What are believed to be females have a much shorter crest.

One of the most unusual duckbilled dinosaurs found in Alberta, Parasaurolophus had a sistinctive tube-like crest projecting behind its head. Nasal passages which ran through the crest may have been used to make sounds.

Armoured Dinosaurs

Encased in an armour of bony plates and spikes, **ankylosaurs** were probably safe from all but the most desperate predator. Even their eyelids were made of bone. Safe in their armour, these were plant eaters. There were two kinds. One had bony armour on its back and nasty spikes sticking out from its shoulders. Although the other group lacked spikes, its tail ended in a crushing club. *Edmontonia* shows the well-developed spikes of the first group.

One of four fleshed-out dinosaurs on view in the Museum's dinosaur gallery, Edmontonia was an armoured dinosaur that flourished in Alberta near the end of the Cretaceous.

Stegoceras – a small pachycephalsaur.

Bird mimics

Long legs, long tails and long flexible necks characterize the bird-mimic dinosaurs, or **ornithomimids**. They were probably the most graceful of the dinosaurs found in Alberta. They were toothless, and many of their bones were hollow. Their feet were clearly built for rapid movement, with long toes and even longer bones in the upper foot. The construction of the pelvis allowed for a rapid leg swing, further suggestion that the ornithomimids were built for speed.

About four meters long, *Ornithomimus* may have robbed the nests of other dinosaurs.

Struthiomimus was stronger and heavier than the other bird-mimic dinosaurs.

Peering over Late Cretaceous vegetation, an ornithomimid surveys Museum visitors.

Small Carnivores

Fossils of small carnivorous dinosaurs are rare in Alberta, even though fragmentary remains indicate that many different kinds lived here.

Dromaeosaurus was a fierce, agile carnivore known from remains of the skull and scattered bones.

Ornitholestes may have hunted lizards and other small animals and scavenged to supplement its diet.

Saurornitholestes is best known from part of a single skeleton although isolated teeth and bones have also been found.

Caenagnathus is known only from scanty remains, some of which are so bird-like they were first mistaken for an ancient bird's.

In a scene on display at the Museum's Field Station in Dinosaur Provincial Park, a pack of dromaeosaurs brings down a duckbilled dinosaur.

Alberta Under Water

Through most of the Cretaceous, a shallow seaway covered the Western Interior of North America. It stretched from the Arctic Ocean to the Gulf of Mexico. At times, it virtually covered the entire province of Alberta.

The Bearpaw was the last of these seas to flood Alberta. When it receded some 70 million years ago, it left a thick layer of marine deposits we call the Bearpaw Formation. These dark shales form the base of the hoodoos east of Drumheller.

The Bearpaw Sea supported a rich diversity of life. Some of its inhabitants were immobile, filtering small particles of food out of the water. Some, like the crayfish, survive today. Others, **ammonites** among them, do not. Clams moved through the mud, their burrows now preserved as trace fossils. The thick oyster beds near Drumheller originated at this time. Worms burrowed through the substrate and **baculites** hung overhead or jetted backwards through the water. Many-armed cuttlefish were preyed upon by large marine lizards — the **mosasaurs**, close relatives of the modern Komodo dragon. Sharks and **plesiosaurs** were other predators in the Bearpaw Sea.

Large carnivores

Although the small flesh-eating dinosaurs were diverse and dangerous, Cretaceous Alberta was ruled by members of the family Tyrannosauridae. This group is distinguished by large size and relatively tiny front limbs.

Clothed once again in flesh and skin, the Museum's mascot, "Lillian" strides through a reconstructed Cretaceous landscape. Except for the colour of her skin, she is based on detailed scientific evidence.

Albertosaurus, the "Alberta lizard", was among the most fearsome predators in Cretaceous Alberta. Almost 10 metres long, it is the most common of the large carnivores found here. Smaller but longer-limbed than Tyrannosaurus, Albertosaurus was probably a mobile hunter.

A close relative of Albertosaurus, Tyrannosaurus appeared at the end of the Cretaceous. The largest meat-eater ever to inhabit the Earth, it is perhaps fitting that it appeared at the very end of the dinosaurs' 150 million year reign. The Museum's specimen was excavated along the Red Deer River north of the Museum.

Mosasaurus (large lizards with powerful jaws and sharp teeth).

Clothed once again in flesh and skin, the Museum's mascot, "Lillian" strides through reconstructed Cretaceous landscape. Except for the colour of her skin, she is based on detailed scientific evidence.

THE END OF THE DINOSAURS

Extinction is a natural result of evolution. More than 90 percent of all species that ever evolved have disappeared. Few of these disappearances fascinate us as much as the extinction of the dinosaurs some 64 million years ago. What happened?

Many extinction theories have arisen. Some propose dinosaurs died out because they could no longer adapt to changes in their physical environment. Changes may have occurred in temperature, rainfall, sea level, atmospheric pressure or composition, ocean currents, length of seasons, even the amount of sunlight Earth received.

Accidental death may have resulted from such catastrophes as volcanoes, earthquakes, radiation, or drastic changes in living conditions caused by changes in the Earth's orbits. Perhaps an extraterrestrial body smashed into the Earth.

Diseases and hormone imbalances, infertility and even constipation have been suggested. Perhaps dinosaurs over-ate, thus destroying their food supply and eventually dying of starvation. Perhaps birds or mammals ate their eggs. Perhaps new species of flowering plants poisoned them. General boredom and world-weariness have been cited as less plausible reasons for their decline.

Scientists give greatest credence to the idea that changing climatic conditions caused dinosaur species to decline in number and diversity throughout the late Mesozoic. Some catastrophic event may have hastened their demise but the writing was clearly on the wall for millions of years.

Still, no theory has answered all the questions. As fossils reveal more about dinosaurs and past environments, we hope that the details of dinosaur extinction may become apparent. Perhaps, however, it will always remain a mystery.

The K/T Boundary

In the badlands north of the Museum lies an inconspicuous line. Next to a coal seam and rich in the tell-tale element iridium, this reddish line marks the end of an era. Below it are the remains of dinosaurs, mixed with the fossilized remains of the animals that shared their world. Above it is a new world. Although many organisms survived the extinctions at the Cretaceous-Tertiary Boundary, dinosaurs didn't. This line marks the end of their era.

THE CENOZOIC ERA

64 – 1.7 million years ago

The Cenozoic Era saw the birth of the modern world. Continents had drifted into relatively familiar positions. Most of our familiar mountain chains were emerging, and the plants and animals were becoming increasingly recognizable.

It was the Age of Mammals. Appearing at the same time as dinosaurs, mammals had remained small and furtive. Dinosaurs so dominated the world that there was little chance for mammals to expand. Nonetheless, even before dinosaurs went into decline, mammals were on the increase. As the great reptiles disappeared, mammals were poised to take over.

The early Cenozoic combined the strange and the familiar. For mammals it was a time of experimentation and diversification.

As the Cenozoic Era progressed, increasingly familiar mammals emerged. Bats appeared tully formed, while pri-mates gradually assumed a modern appearance. *Uintatherium*, a large ungainly plant-eater, was a failed experiment, giving way to cloven-hoofed vegetarians, the forerunners of deer, camels and cattle.

Many modern-looking freshwater fish swam in the North American lakes during the first half of the Cenozoic Era. Insects, birds and turtles inhabited the surrounding land. Forests of giant conifers and meadows of flowering plants flourished under temperate skies. More than 200 cm of rain fell every year, an amount similar to many parts of the British Columbia coast today.

Like many large mammals, Brontotheres may have engaged in territorial battles. Such contests are rarely fatal, but some specimens have been found with damaged ribs, perhaps the result of these disputes.

The Museum's award-winning Cenozoic exhibit shows mammals taking on an increasingly modern appearance.

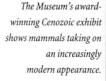

The development of the horse provides a classic example of evolution.
Hyracotherium — first known horse.

Horse Sense

The first known horse, *Hyracotherium*, about half the size of a standard poodle, appeared 55 million years ago at the start of the Eocene Epoch. It had three toes on each hind foot and four toes on its front feet.

One of its descendants was the slightly larger *Mesohippus*. It had an enlarged middle toe encased in a tiny hoof, but retained a side toe on either side.

As horses evolved into more modern forms, the side toes were further reduced, and a hard hoof perfectly suited to running across grasslands appeared. With the shift to a diet of grass, horses developed the deep, long jaws, broad crushing molars and large incisors ideal for feeding on such an abrasive diet.

Although a native North American, the horse disappeared from our continent, leaving remains dated at 9,000 years ago in Alberta. Europeans re-introduced the horse over 400 years ago.

Hyracotherium   *Mesohippus*   *Merychippus*   *Pliohippus*   *Equus*

Plants adapted to a gradually cooling climate. Fossil leaves and seeds on display in the Museum show a gradual shift from plants that favoured warm, humid conditions to plants better able to withstand cool, dry periods. While non-flowering plants like ferns and pines still grew here, flowering plants were evolving quickly.

Grass became a dominant component of modern landscapes. As grasslands expanded, grazing animals developed. Camels originated in North America and took advantage of the developing grasslands. Meat-eaters too evolved new forms to compete effectively in the new environment.

The North American plains continued to cool in the latter half of the Cenozoic. Spreading south from the Hudson's Bay area and eastwards from the Rocky Mountains, great ice sheets scraped across the northern half of our continent four times during the last two million years.

An experiment on the plains, Synthetoceras developed an unusual two-pronged horn on its nose. A grass-eater and a speedy runner, this deer-like animal lived in North America some five million years ago.

Gomphthotherium - closely related to Mastodons entered North America from Eurasia during the Miocene.

North America has been covered in ice many times. We may, in fact, now be in a brief interlude of a much longer ice age. The Museum's Ice Age display explains the effects of the most recent glacial advances.

Falling sea levels during parts of the ice age periodically exposed a narrow land bridge between Asia and North America. Across the bridge moved many living things. North American natives, including camels, horses and cheetahs migrated to Asia. Mastodon, mammoth, bison and muskox crossed the other way. Behind them, pursuing an important food supply, came our own species, *Homo sapiens.*

A modern buffalo attempts to dodge Smilodon's attack.

Poised above fossil prairie dog burrows, a small ground sloth slowly waves a long-clawed paw at departing visitors. Some ground sloths grew to the size of elephants.

58

A Species Known as Man

Through fossils, we can trace our own history back to primate ancestors. Similarities in muscle and bone structure, shared blood types, behavioural patterns, and susceptibility to the same diseases clearly link humans and their primate relatives.

An early man-like ape about the size of a baboon, *Ramapithicus* inhabited the borders of forests in Asia and Africa about 15 million years ago.

Several of *Australopithicus* appear to have inhabited the African savannah seven to four million years ago. They had relatively large brains and were the first hominid known to have walked erect.

The first member of our genus, tiny *Homo habilis* appeared in Africa some seven million years ago.

Homo erectus possessed a larger brain than any previous hominid, walked upright, made and used tools, and may have developed a rudimentary speech.

Large-brained and flat-faced, *Homo sapiens* migrated into North America across the Bering Land Bridge at least 30,000 years ago. Human culture spread across the continent, leaving evidence of an increasingly sophisticated civilization.

The Unseen Museum

As in all major museums, activities behind the scenes are vital to the success of public displays and programmes. The Royal Tyrrell Museum carries out extensive collection and research in many areas of palaeontology.

Among its researchers are:

Dr. Phil Currie is in charge of Dinosaur Research at the Museum, his primary interest is carnivorous dinosaurs.

Fossil turtles exert a powerful fascination for **Dr. Don Brinkman.**

Dr. Betsy Nicholls is a specialist in marine reptiles.

Dr. Paul Johnston concentrates on invertebrates, especially clams.

Dr. Dennis Braman is in charge of palaeobotony – he specializes in fossil pollens and is working on the mystery of the Cretaceous - Tertiary Boundary.

Andy Neuman studies early Mesozoic fish.

Dr. Dave Eberth, a geologist, explores the relationships between fossils and the sediments in which they are found.

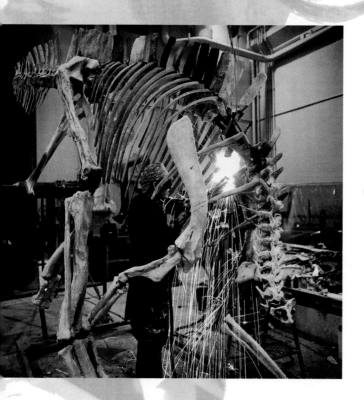

Many other activities are unseen by most Museum visitors. In the laboratories, museum technicians carefully remove delicate fossil specimens from the surrounding rock. Molds are prepared and casts made for study, exchange and exhibit. Conservators and cataloguers keep track of the more than 100,000 fossils in the Royal Tyrrell's collection.

Designers, illustrators, educators, technicians and many others prepare the exhibits, programmes and do much more that distinguishes the Royal Tyrrell Museum.

Wait... There's more!

Special activities and events, plus year-round services are also part of what makes your visit to the Royal Tyrrell Museum one you won't forget.

During your visit, watch for announcements inviting you to take part in the day's activities — it could be a special lecture with a visiting scientist, a hike in the badlands, gallery games, or programmes presented by our roving interpreters.

The Museum is wheelchair accessible and both wheelchairs and strollers are available at our front desk. For our winter visitors, a battery-charging service is also available.

When you're ready for a snack, light lunch or a hot entree — remember our full service cafeteria is open year round. On a hot day, enjoy something cold on the outdoor patio overlooking the Museum's picturesque pools.

Before you leave, be sure to stop at the Royal Tyrrell Museum Shop for souvenirs of your visit. You will find everything from Museum-quality fossil replicas to a range of dinosaur T-shirt designs.

DAY DiGS

COME WITH US ON A REAL DINOSAUR DIG

Buried in the badlands surrounding the Royal Tyrrell Museum are dinosaur fossils that have been concealed for more than 70 million years.

Now you can experience the thrill of uncovering these ancient remains when you come on a Day Dig. This new programme lets you spend a full day as part of a quarry operation or enjoy a 90 minute guided tour of the excavation site. Reservations can be made in advance or during your visit to the Museum. Just remember your hat, walking shoes and bring your camera, because without pictures your friends will never believe you!

Special Exhibits

Less than a year ago, Dr. Philip Currie, together with scientists from China and the U.S., announced a landmark discovery: Dinosaur fossils with feathers had been found in northeastern China.

Now China's Feathered dinosaurs are coming to the Royal Tyrrell Museum. This exhibition of rare specimens and artists' models depicts a critical period in dinosaur evolution.

The Royal Tyrrell Museum is the final stop on the exhibits' North American tour, organized by the National Geographic Society, and will be the only place in Canada where these amazing fossils can be seen.

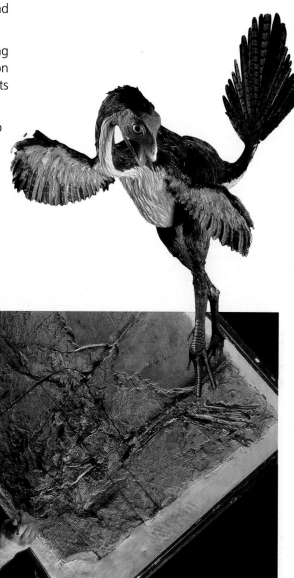

DINOSAUR PROVINCIAL PARK

Dinosaur Provincial Park gained its international reputation and designation as a UNESCO World Heritage Site primarily because of the large number of dinosaur fossils exposed in its deeply eroded badlands.

Many of the specimens displayed at the Royal Tyrrell Museum come from Dinosaur Provincial Park – the Museum conducts major digs there every summer. To support its collecting activities, the museum established a Field Station in the heart of the badlands.

Some 120 kilometres southeast of the museum, the field station not only supports the summer field season, but assists in the preservation of fossil resources and displays significant finds in a small but exciting exhibit hall. The displays present a picture of what the region looked like 75 million years ago, when the fossils were living creatures.